THINGS THAT GO

ACTIVITY BOOK

PaRragon

Bath • New York • Cologne • Melbourne • Delhi
Hong Kong • Shenzhen • Singapore

Different Diggers

Finish the diggers with scoops, wheels, caterpillar tracks, and more.

Train Station

The train is about to leave the station. Fill the platform with passengers, and add windows and wheels to the carriages with your stickers.

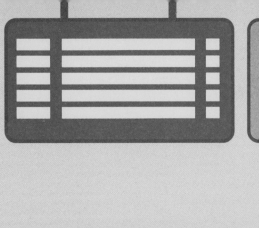

Find and circle the passenger with the big green suitcase.

24

Down at the Docks

It's a busy day down at the docks. Load up the cargo ship with containers and barrels.

Ambulance Maze

The ambulance needs to get to the hospital fast! Can you find your way through the maze as quickly as possible?

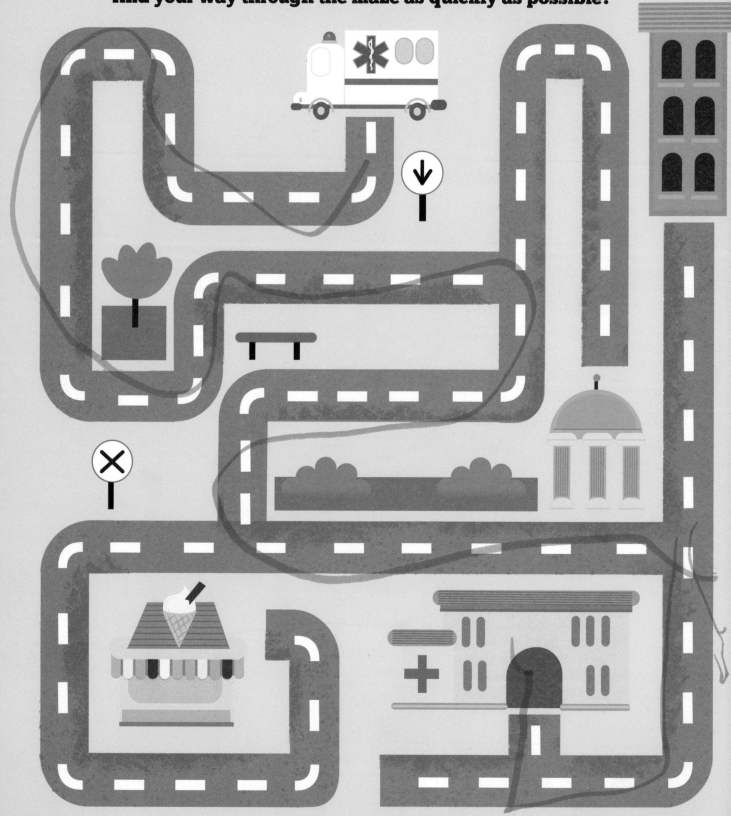

Stop! Police!

The red car is driving too fast down a busy highway. Add police cars chasing the car, but watch out for other traffic!

How many green cars are on the highway?

POLICE

POLICE

Roadwork

Fixing roads is hard work! Add lots of busy road workers and construction vehicles.

Put pipes in the holes dug by the diggers.

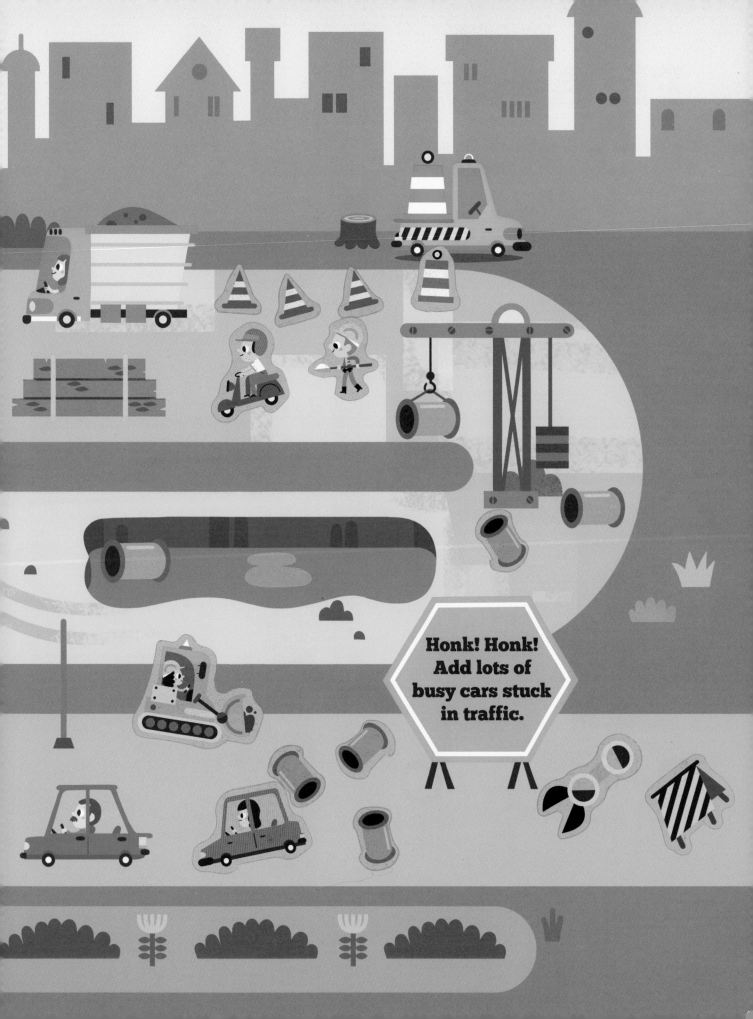

Fly Away

It's time to fly off for a vacation!
Fill the sky with more planes.

Add passengers
ready to board
the plane.

Put more suitcases on the conveyor belt. Speed things up with extra workers in orange vests!

Subway Stops

Help this train find the way
to stop number 5.

Tire Treads

Each vehicle's tires have left a different pattern of tread. Fill the gaps with your stickers.

Fill Up the Ferry

The ferry goes back and forth across the harbor all day long.
How many cars can you get safely to the other side?

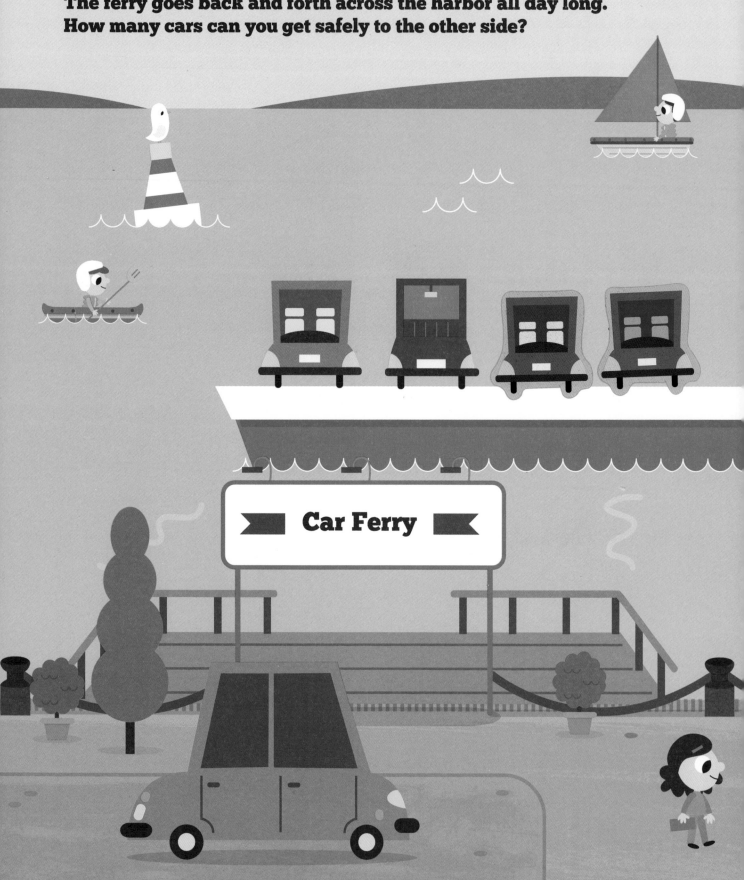

Car Ferry

Tough Truck

The truck driver needs to make a delivery this morning.
Use your stickers to complete the controls.

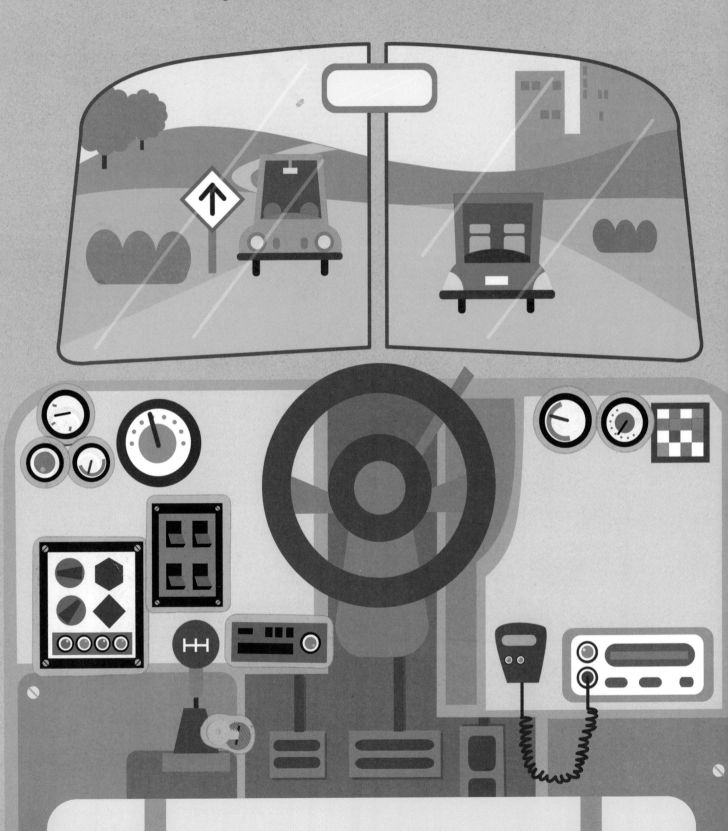

Loading Up

Can you spot five differences between these two pictures?

Add a truck wheel each time you spot a difference.

Hot Air Balloons

Fill the sky with lots of bright balloons.

Can you spot the two matching pairs of balloons?

Give this hot air balloon an exciting design.

Fun in the Fields

It's harvest time. Fill the fields with a combine harvester, tractors, bales of hay, and crops.

The birds are trying to eat the corn! How many birds can you see?

Match the Shadows

Draw lines to match each farm vehicle with its shadow.

Add a bale of hay for each shadow you match.

Big Tractor Coloring

Color in the big tractor. Draw yourself in the driver's seat.

Traffic Jam

Uh-oh. There's a huge traffic jam on the highway. Can you see what caused it?

Fill the road with more waiting cars.

Beep! Beep!

Beep! Beep!

Can you spot these vehicles in the traffic? Check off each one when you find it.

Bike Trail

Put your foot down and add some zooming
quad bikes and dirt bikes to the trail.

Monster Truck Show

The monster truck rally is just about to start. Use your stickers to add awesome designs to the trucks.

Can you find and circle these fans in the crowd?

Add more old cars for the trucks to crush.

Busy Buses

It's a busy day and lots of people are waiting for the bus.
Match the numbers to park the buses at the right stops.

Use your
stickers to
complete
the bus.

Water Sports

Add lots of people trying different water sports on the lake. Some like to ride in speedboats and on jet skis. Some like to waterski or parasail.

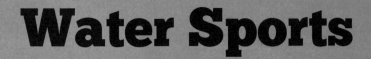

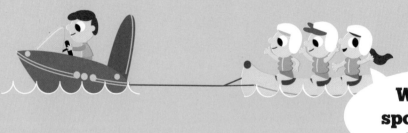

Which water sport would you like to try?

Trolley Lines

The trolleys can take you all over town. Match the numbers and add the missing trolley stickers to the right lines.

line 1

line 2

line 3

1

Which trolley goes where? Add a matching number sticker next to each picture below.

A

B

C

Answers: A-3, B-1, C-2.

At the Campground

Let's set up camp in the woods. Fill the scene with more motor homes and some tents.

Don't forget to include some campers.

Ice Cream Time

Draw and color your favorite ice creams
and ice pops on the side of the truck.

Steamroller Maze

The steamroller is working hard to flatten the unfinished roads.
Guide it all the way to the red house to smooth out the bumps.

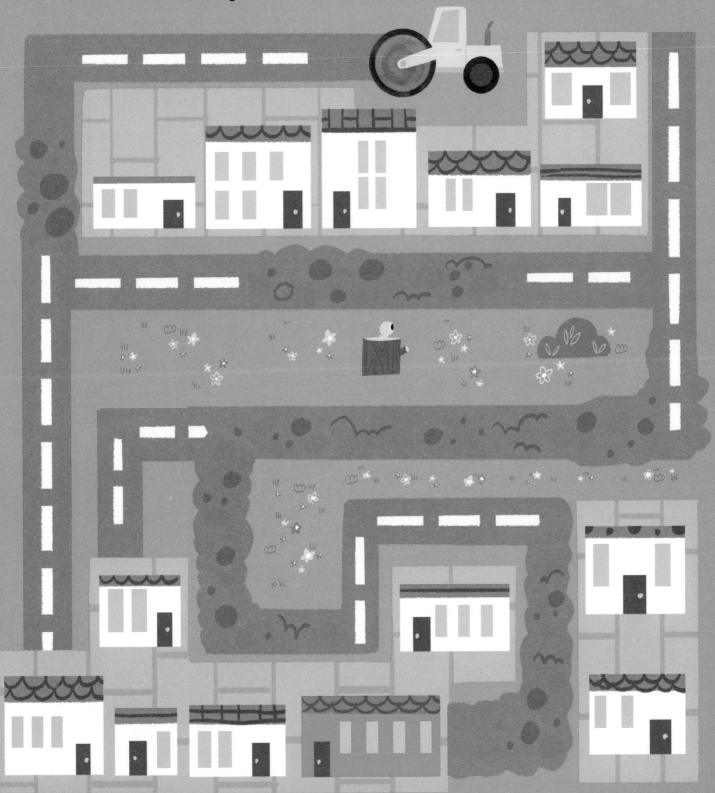

Swamp Ride

These children are enjoying an adventure in the swamp. Add more airboats, kayaks, and canoes to the scene.

How many sneaky alligators can you find?

Delivery Time

The delivery trucks are filling up with boxes. Can you add
the yellow, green, and red boxes in the right trailers?

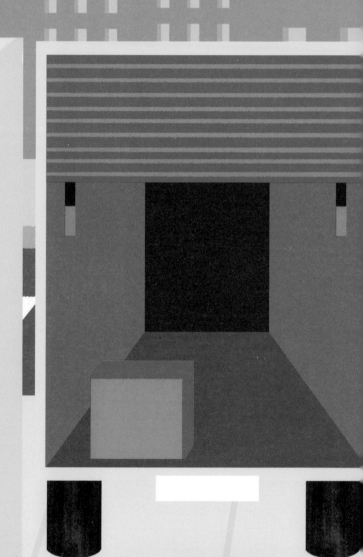

**Add more workers
to help load up.**

Scootering and Skating

It's busy in the skate park today. Add lots of children scootering, riding, skating, and zooming around!

**Find the matching
pair of bicycles and the
matching pair of scooters.**

Timber Trucks

The timber company needs to get more logs to its factory. Add trucks filled with logs to the roads.

1 2
3

Oh, no! All the bridges over the river are missing. Build bridges for the trucks with your stickers.

Forest Fire! Help!

Help! There's a fire in the woods! Use your stickers to add the fire crew putting the fire out.

Can you see what might have started the fire?

Spotting Safari

Fill the savanna with more safari jeeps and animals.

Can you spy a lion hiding? Circle it.

Which animal stands on one leg in the watering hole?

Answer: Flamingo

Mountain Rescue

The mountain rescue team is searching for two lost climbers. Can you help find them?

Acrobatic Air Show

Lots of excited people have come to see the air show. Use
your plane stickers to make an exciting display for the crowd.

Let's Go Karting

Add lots of karts racing around the track!

Finish

Fill the crowd with more excited people.

Under the Sea

This submarine is getting ready to dive deep underwater.
Put more portholes on the side, filled with smiling faces.

Fill the sea
with more
underwater creatures.

**Add a propeller
to power the
submarine.**

Factory Fun

There have been lots of deliveries today. Add more
workers and forklift trucks to help stack the boxes.

Can you find
and circle the
red box?

Building Site

A new school is being built in the city. Add cement mixers ready to pour the foundations and some builders to get the job done.

One of the builders
has lost his hard hat.
Can you find and
circle it for him?

Mega Mine

Work never stops at the mine. Each vehicle has its own job
to do—digging, scooping, and moving. Add dump trucks
to help move earth and rocks away.

Coal Truck Coloring

Color in the truck to help the miners get the job done.

Cruise Ship

Hop aboard! The round-the-world cruise is about to set sail.
Can you add more lifeboats before it leaves the port?

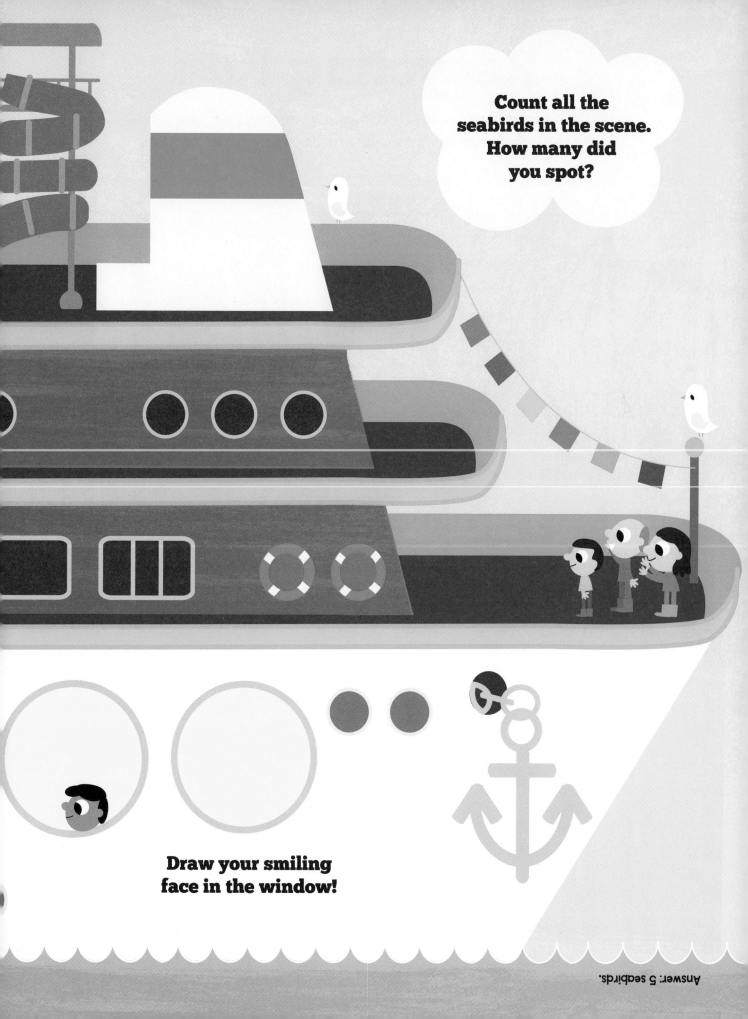

Count all the seabirds in the scene. How many did you spot?

Draw your smiling face in the window!

Recycling Run

It's recycling collection day. Drive past all the carts
to pick them up, then get to the recycling center.

Find and circle the moldy
old sandwich. Gross!

Sort the Recyclables

Help the workers put the recyclables into the
different containers with your stickers.

Odd Bike Out

Which motorbike is the odd one out?

3 ... 2 ... 1 ... Blast Off!

Use your stickers to prepare this rocket for a space adventure.

Space Travel

Let's blast into space! Add rockets and satellites.

Send more astronauts on a spacewalk.

Can you spot an
alien spaceship?

Dune Buggy Race

These drivers are dashing across the desert.
Add more dune buggies to the race.

Can you spot a
desert fox watching
the action? Circle it.

Train Engines

Can you spot five differences between these two pictures?

Add a train engine sticker each time you spot a difference.

Load the Crane

This crane has arrived on site ready to lift and move crates, containers, and more.

Car Carrier Combos

The car carrier is loading up. Add the missing vehicles so they're all in matching pairs.

Add more mechanics and toolboxes to the scene.

Bumper Cars

The carnival has come to town! Fill the
track with lots of whizzing bumper cars.

Add cotton candy and hot dog stands
ready to serve the hungry children.

Let's Go Racing!

Get your engines roaring and fill up the track with zooming race cars! **GO, GO, GO!**

Can you spot
the cameraperson
filming the race?

Helicopter Game

**These pilots can't remember where to land their helicopters.
Follow the line from each one to its helipad.**

Land each
helicopter by adding
a matching sticker
on each helipad.

Chopper Trouble

Can you spot five differences between these two pictures?

Add a helicopter sticker here each time you spot a difference.

Demolition Site

Bang! Crash! Boom! The demolition workers have been busy today! Add diggers and piles of rubble ready to be scooped up and taken away.

Let's Go Surfing

Surf's up! Add lots more surfers and windsurfers enjoying the waves at the beach.

How many
kitesurfers can you count?

How many people are
wearing headphones?

Answer: 2 people.

Snowy Day

Help clear the roads of snow with more
snowplows so that people can get moving.

Add some children playing in the snow.

Can you spot all these things in the snow? Add a snow shovel below each one when you find it.

Yacht Coloring

Add a sticker design to the sails, then color the boat.